www.heinemannlibrary.co.uk
Visit our website to find out more information about Heinemann Library books.

To order:
☎ Phone +44 (0) 1865 888066
🖹 Fax +44 (0) 1865 314091
💻 Visit www.heinemannlibrary.co.uk

Heinemann Library is an imprint of **Capstone Global Library Limited**, a company incorporated in England and Wales having its registered office at 7 Pilgrim Street, London, EC4V 6LB – Registered company number: 6695582

"Heinemann Library" is a registered trademark of Pearson Education Limited, under licence to Capstone Global Library Limited

Text © Capstone Global Library Limited 2009
First published by Weldon Owen Education Inc. in 2008
First published in hardback in the United Kingdom in 2009
The moral rights of the proprietor have been asserted.

Project edited by Briony Hill
Written by Avelyn Davidson
Edited by Mary Atkinson
Designed by Juliet Hughes and Matthew Alexander
Original illustrations © Weldon Owen Education Inc. 2008
Illustrated by Edwina Cosme
Picture research by Jamshed Mistry
Originated by Weldon Owen Education Inc.

Printed in China through Colorcraft Ltd., Hong Kong

Acknowledgements
We would like to thank the following for permission to reproduce photographs: AAP Image: AFP (woman holding orangutan, p. 21); AP (injured camel, p. 20); Human Battery Cage Group/Shane Dalgleish (battery hen protestors, p. 17); Ian Massam (visitor with dogs, p. 15); iStockPhoto.com ('thinking cap' hat, all pages); Jennifer and Brian Lupton (students, pp. 22–23); Photolibrary (p. 16; p. 18; protest banner, p. 19; protestors, p. 21); Riccardo Agnelli/www.straydogsturkey.org (cover; p. 1; girl with puppy, dogs in compound, pp. 2–3; p. 13; Perihan Agnelli, p. 15; p. 24); Tranz: Corbis (p. 14; volunteer feeding rhinoceros, p. 20; orangutan, p. 21; ruins, background, pp. 22–23); Reuters (elephants in traffic, p. 20; woman rescuing dog, p. 17); © WSPA: The World Society for the Protection of Animals (muzzled bear, p. 19; WSPA vet, Bangladesh, p. 19)

ISBN 978-0-431179-70-4 (hardback)
13 12 11 10 09
10 9 8 7 6 5 4 3 2 1

British Library Cataloguing in Publication Data
Davidson, Avelyn.
  To the rescue: animal rights. – (Worldscapes)
179.3-dc22
A full catalogue record for this book is available from the British Library.

Disclaimer

To the Rescue

Written by Avelyn Davidson
Illustrated by Edwina Cosme

Turkey

My name is Melis. I live in Fethiye, in Turkey. Turkey has a problem with stray animals. Recently, our class visited the Fethiye Rescue Centre. We learned about a rescue programme that was started there. We held the puppies. We also helped paint a wall at one of the new shelters.

Contents

Look for the **Thinking Cap**.
When you see this picture, you will find
a problem to think about and write about.

The yellow dog

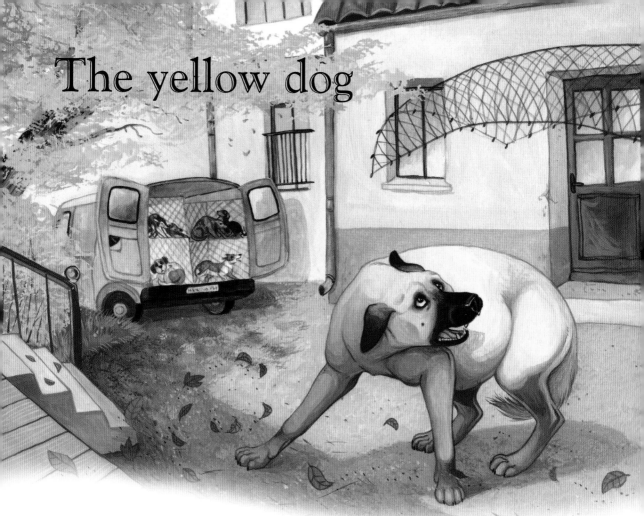

Trapped

The last of the autumn leaves whirled down the street in Fethiye. The icy wind blew on the yellow dog where she lay curled under the floor of an old **veranda**. She was cold, and her pups were due soon. Her tummy rumbled with hunger. She needed to look for food. She stretched and sniffed the air. She could smell snow coming, but not much else.

She thought it odd that there were no street dogs around. Then she heard barking and whimpering coming from a side street. The yellow dog knew that something was amiss and turned to run. Suddenly, a net was hurled over her. She struggled and snarled, but she was trapped. The yellow dog was pushed into a van already filled with other dogs.

veranda open porch attached to a house, often with a roof

'That's the last of them,' said a voice.

'This one's pregnant,' said another voice.

'Tough,' said the first voice. 'She won't last long.'

The van, loaded with dogs, rattled down the street. The yellow dog was jammed against the wire door.

She trembled with fear. But she stayed alert, watching where she was going and sniffing the air.

Before long, the van was climbing a steep, mountain road, and snow began to fall heavily. After about four hours, the van shuddered to a halt. The wire door was thrown open. Someone grabbed the yellow dog by the scruff of the neck and threw her roughly into the snow. The other dogs followed.

'They'll never make it back from here,' said one of the men. Then they got into the van and drove away.

Abandoned

Frightened and cold, the dogs shivered. They whined and yelped and lay huddled where they were thrown. The yellow dog looked around with her intelligent brown eyes. Somehow she knew she had to get moving.

She dragged herself to her feet. The tyre marks of the van were clear in the snow. The yellow dog put her nose to the ground and trotted off.

Before long her paws were frozen, and she was exhausted from the cold, thin air. She needed to rest.

Not far below her she could see a group of snow-covered fir trees. Instinctively, she turned towards them, seeking shelter. The snow was not so thick beneath the trees.

The dog dug her way in between the roots. She licked and licked her paws until the feeling returned. Then she sank into an exhausted sleep. When she woke, she was snowed in.

Again, instinct told her to get moving. Reluctantly, she began to dig her way out. The world was white as far as she could see.

The tyre marks had vanished. But still she knew she had to keep moving downhill. She broke into a run and set off down the mountain.

Abandoning street dogs in the mountains in winter has been a common method used by towns in Turkey and Greece to address the stray dog problem.

Exhausted

For the next three days, the dog kept moving down the mountain. She was cold and weak from hunger, but she knew that she had to find food and shelter. In the white world around her nothing moved, except for a hawk circling lazily overhead, watching her. The dog sunk to the ground as the hawk dropped lower and lower towards her. When it was just above her head, the dog leaped into the air and grabbed it.

The hawk sunk its talons into the dog's shoulder, but it was no match for the starving dog.

Hungrily, she devoured most of the hawk. Then she picked up its carcass and moved on.

Towards nightfall, the yellow dog spotted some timber protruding through the snow. It was a **goatherd**'s summer hut.

Gathering up her strength, the dog dug a tunnel into the hut. Wearily, she dragged herself and the hawk into the shelter and collapsed onto the ground.

Around midday the next day, four pups were born.

The tired mother licked them until they were clean and warm. Then she fell into an exhausted sleep.

goatherd person who herds goats

Shot

The yellow dog lived in the goatherd's hut with her pups for the next eight weeks. She hunted rabbits for food. She licked the snow to get water.

One day, she sensed that the weather was changing. Icicles around the hut were starting to thaw. It was getting warmer.

It was time to move on.

With her pups in tow, she set off down the snowy mountainside.

Finding food became easier but more dangerous. One day when she was raiding a hen house, the farmer appeared with a gun.

'Get out of here you **vermin**!' he yelled, as the dog leaped the fence with a hen in her mouth.

There was a great bang, and the dog felt a searing pain through her left ear. Panic stricken, she ran back to where she had left the pups.

She rubbed her ear in the snow; it soon turned red with her blood. Again and again, she rubbed her ear until it felt numb.

No one had followed her, so she and her pups settled down to a hard-earned meal.

For the next two weeks, the yellow dog guided her pups down the mountain. One night, she saw the lights of Fethiye in the distance. She was nearly home.

Before long, she was back in familiar territory. She gathered her pups under her old veranda, then lay down beside them.

She had brought them hundreds of kilometres home.

vermin pest

Saved

A face appeared near the veranda. 'Here they are,' said a voice. 'This is the dog we have all heard about. Look. Her ear is wounded.'

A hand reached in and pulled her out. Other hands pulled out the pups. Frightened, the dog struggled and fought, but she and the pups were placed in a van.

The yellow dog trembled and sniffed the air. But this time they did not head up the mountain. They went down the coast road. They turned up a long driveway. The yellow dog heard other dogs barking. She smelled safety, not danger. Gentle hands soothed her. Kind voices spoke of her long journey.

'We will have no trouble finding homes for these beautiful pups,' said a woman's voice.

'The yellow dog will have a home here with us for the rest of her life. We'll tell her story to all the students who visit us. We want a better and kinder future for all street dogs.'

Put on your thinking cap

Write down your thoughts about the following questions. Then discuss them with a classmate.

1. Why do you think the street dogs were collected and dumped far away in the mountains in winter?

2. Do you think this was **humane** treatment for the dogs? Why or why not?

3. How are stray animals treated where you live?

humane kind

'The Yellow Dog' is a true story. The yellow dog (above) lives in the sanctuary at Fethiye. Her pups (below) found good homes.

What's the issue?

Stray dogs and cats have been a problem in Turkey for many years. Hundreds of animals roam the streets looking for handouts of food from restaurants and homes. Many of the animals look diseased and are full of ticks and other parasites. Others look like well cared for pets. Few of the dogs are vicious. Most of them are just hungry and in need of care.

In the past, the dogs were often poisoned or shot. This upset many local people and tourists. The next strategy was to round them up and dump them in the mountains in winter. There they soon died from cold or hunger.

Today, thanks to many hard-working, caring people, solutions to the stray dog problem include humane programmes. The dogs are rounded up and taken to a clinic, where they are **neutered**. They are treated for infections and parasites, such as ticks. They are also vaccinated against rabies. Then they are tagged and returned to the streets, where they live out their lives without breeding more stray dogs.

neuter to treat an animal so that it will not have babies

In 2004, Turkey passed an Animal Protection Law. The law requires that all local authorities adopt the neuter-and-return method of dealing with stray animals. The law also requires all pet animals to be neutered. If people cannot afford the cost of neutering their pet, local clinics will do it for free. This method is proving very successful in reducing the numbers of stray dogs and cats.

A visitor receives a warm welcome from the dogs.

The centre in Fethiye

The neuter-and-return programme was the idea of Perihan Agnelli, who was appalled at the way dogs and cats were treated in her hometown of Fethiye.

Agnelli set up a clinic and animal sanctuary, and she hired a vet to work with her. She persuaded the local mayor to let her try the neuter-and-return programme. The programme was a great success. Soon other towns adopted the idea.

Today, many people visit the centre in Fethiye, which is set in 106 acres (43 hectares) of forest. They learn how to care for dogs and cats and learn about the neuter-and-return programme. The centre is where the yellow dog is living out her life.

Perihan Agnelli

Animal welfare

In many parts of the world, animal welfare and animal rights are important issues. In other places, animals are treated **inhumanely**. Unwanted kittens and puppies are dumped or harmed. Certain breeds of dogs are raised for fighting and are seriously injured or killed. Racing animals that no longer perform well, such as greyhounds, are often put down. Fortunately, all around the world, organisations and groups of volunteers provide shelters and care for mistreated or unwanted animals. Such organisations also educate people about animal rights.

The Greyhound Adoption League of South Florida is a non-profit organisation that finds caring homes for retired greyhounds.

inhumanely cruelly

Houston Society for the Prevention of Cruelty to Animals (HSPCA) played a key role in rescuing and caring for animals after Hurricane Katrina.

Put on your thinking cap

Write down your thoughts about the following questions. Then discuss them with a classmate.

1. What animal rescue organisations are in your area?

2. How do the organisations get funding?

3. What are some ways that you or your class could help? Do you think sponsoring an animal is a good idea? Why or why not?

4. What animal protection agencies are in your country?

Many organisations protest animal mistreatment. Protestors from one organisation do not believe that chickens should be confined in small cages just to lay eggs for humans; they have shut themselves in a cage to make their point to passers-by.

To the rescue

In many countries around the world, wild animals are becoming increasingly endangered. Their habitats are being destroyed or reduced through farming and forestry. Many are slaughtered for their meat or skins. Others are captured and sold to zoos and pet shops.

Care for the Wild International (CWI) is an animal welfare and conservation charity that funds projects around the world. It acts as a global voice for wildlife. Through research and education, it exposes animal cruelty and wildlife crimes. It also funds projects to rehabilitate sick or injured animals. It provides sanctuaries for those animals that cannot be returned to the wild. CWI has relieved the suffering of hundreds of animals, including monkeys, bears, elephants and snakes.

Tourists are often the people who report animal cruelty. The CWI investigates reports from tourists.

Baby gorillas orphaned by poaching are cared for in this sanctuary in Rwanda, Africa.

In some places, animals are exploited for entertainment. This young bear was taken from her mother. She was then forced to dance by the use of a thick rope pulled through a hole drilled in her sensitive muzzle.

Scientific research

In many places, animals are used for research. Dogs, cats, rabbits, mice, chimpanzees and other animals are used to test new drugs before they are used on people.

Whether this should be allowed is a big issue internationally. Many people feel that animal testing is a 'necessary evil'. They feel that it is important to keep looking for cures for diseases and illnesses.

Some think that primates should not be used. Others feel that it is wrong to test on any animals. Some people will not buy products, such as shampoos and cosmetics, that have been tested on animals. What do you think?

The World Society for the Protection of Animals (WSPA) works in countries, such as Bangladesh, to help animals affected by floods and other disasters.

Protesting is one way people can voice their opinions.

Animal welfare around the world

No more elephants

MUMBAI, INDIA – The elephants are leaving Mumbai. State authorities have ruled that forcing the animals to walk through traffic on the crowded city streets of India's largest city is inhumane.

Stop primate testing

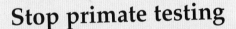

OXFORD, ENGLAND – Students are protesting a new animal research facility proposed for Oxford University. The focus of the protest is strong opposition to primate testing.

Rhino rescue

BOTSWANA – This baby rhinoceros was orphaned after poachers killed its mother for her horn. The baby was taken to a sanctuary, where it is being cared for by wildlife officers.

Camel rescued from minefield

ISRAEL – This injured camel was lifted to safety after it was found wandering in a minefield. Its Bedouin owner no longer wanted the animal because it had been injured.

Vets support move against animal cruelty

ENGLAND – Chief veterinary officers from around the world have officially supported a move towards a Universal Declaration on Animal Welfare at the United Nations. The UK government has also stated its support for improving animal welfare.

Wildlife conservation

VIETNAM – The Vietnamese group Wildlife at Risk warns that illegal wildlife trade in many parts of Asia is almost out of control. This baby orangutan was recently rescued and will go to an animal sanctuary.

What's your opinion?

Turkey is not a very wealthy country. It cannot afford to provide permanent sanctuaries for all its stray dogs and cats. However, it has found a humane method of controlling the problem. Turkey was one of the first countries in the world to introduce the neuter-and-return law.

- Do you think it would be a good idea for all countries to adopt a similar law? Explain your opinion.

- Do you think all pet animals should be neutered? Why or why not?

This law is much kinder than killing unwanted animals. Shelters are full of animals needing homes. If all cats and dogs had to be neutered, it would soon reduce the number of unwanted animals. People who want to breed their animals should have to get a licence.

I think it is a good idea, but it would be very hard to enforce. If we had free vet services for people to get their animals neutered, more people might do this. But it would cost the governments a lot. Our country has a lot of shelters that do a good job finding good homes for animals.

Our dog had puppies recently and we found them all good homes. I would not want to be forced to have her neutered. I think people should have a choice. We need more education through television to tell people about the importance of caring for their pets.

Think tank

1. Find out about a particular animal that needs protection near where you live. What are the issues involved?

2. Collect newspaper clippings of animal rescues or animal rights protests around the world. Which organisations were involved in these rescues and protests? Do you agree with the protestors? Why or why not?

3. How could you or your class help animal rescue organisations?

Do your own research at the library, on the Internet, or with a parent or teacher to find out more about animal rescues and animal rights issues around the world.

Glossary

goatherd person who herds goats

humane kind

inhumanely cruelly

neuter to treat an animal so that it will not have babies

veranda open porch attached to a house, often with a roof

vermin pest

Index